Jingle Bell

CHRISTMAS CAROL COLORING
BY ODESSA BEGAY

LARK

New York

LARK
New York

An Imprint of Sterling Publishing Co., Inc.
1166 Avenue of the Americas
New York, NY 10036

ISBN 978-1-4547-1040-0

Distributed in Canada by Sterling Publishing Co., Inc.
c/o Canadian Manda Group, 664 Annette Street
Toronto, Ontario, Canada M6S 2C8
Distributed in the United Kingdom by GMC Distribution Services
Castle Place, 166 High Street, Lewes, East Sussex, England BN7 1XU
Distributed in Australia by NewSouth Books
45 Beach Street, Coogee, NSW 2034, Australia

For information about custom editions, special sales, and
premium and corporate purchases, please contact Sterling Special Sales
at 800-805-5489 or specialsales@sterlingpublishing.com.

Manufactured in Canada

2 4 6 8 10 9 7 5 3 1

www.larkcrafts.com
www.sterlingpublishing.com

To all the great holiday memories to come

Introduction

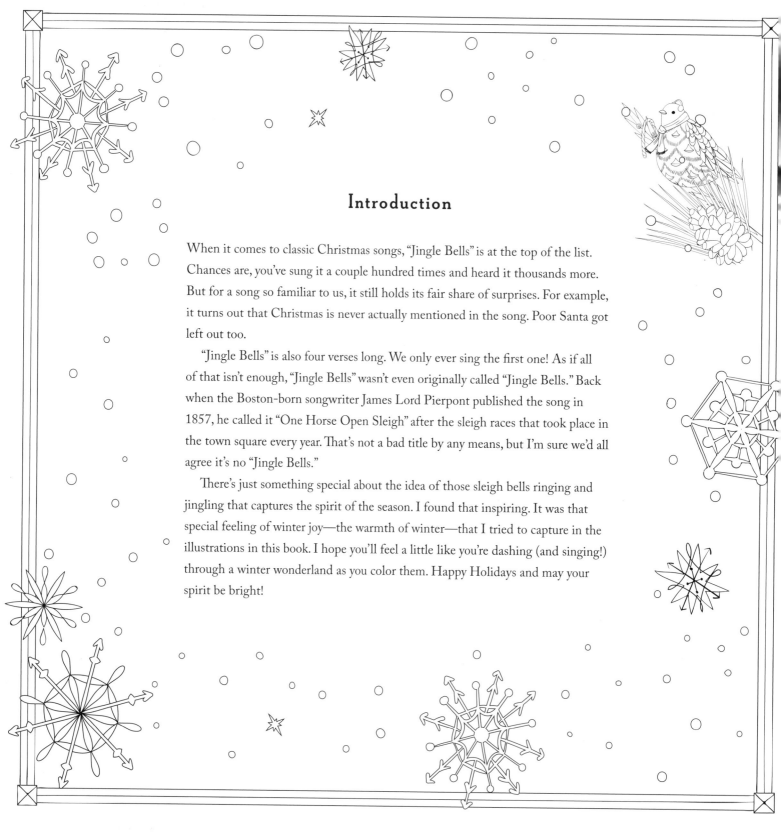

When it comes to classic Christmas songs, "Jingle Bells" is at the top of the list. Chances are, you've sung it a couple hundred times and heard it thousands more. But for a song so familiar to us, it still holds its fair share of surprises. For example, it turns out that Christmas is never actually mentioned in the song. Poor Santa got left out too.

"Jingle Bells" is also four verses long. We only ever sing the first one! As if all of that isn't enough, "Jingle Bells" wasn't even originally called "Jingle Bells." Back when the Boston-born songwriter James Lord Pierpont published the song in 1857, he called it "One Horse Open Sleigh" after the sleigh races that took place in the town square every year. That's not a bad title by any means, but I'm sure we'd all agree it's no "Jingle Bells."

There's just something special about the idea of those sleigh bells ringing and jingling that captures the spirit of the season. I found that inspiring. It was that special feeling of winter joy—the warmth of winter—that I tried to capture in the illustrations in this book. I hope you'll feel a little like you're dashing (and singing!) through a winter wonderland as you color them. Happy Holidays and may your spirit be bright!

and soon, Miss Fanny Bright was seated by my side,

The horse was lean and lank, misfortune seemed his lot

he got into a drifted bank and then we got upsot!

he laughed as there I sprawling lie, but quickly drove away!

About the Author

Odessa loves botanical gardens, animals, and patterns.
Whenever there's an opportunity to combine them, she's
all for it! She is an illustrator and surface pattern designer
currently working on the east coast. To see what she's drawing
now, follow her at instagram.com/odessabegay or check out
her website www.odessabegay.com.